BLACKBERRY FARM

EMILY THE GOAT

Jane Pilgrim

This edition first published in the United Kingdom in 1999 by
Brockhampton Press
20 Bloomsbury Street
London WC1B 3QA
An imprint of the Caxton Publishing Group Ltd.

Reprint 2001 / 2002

© Text copyright MCMLII by Jane Pilgrim
© Illustrations copyright MCMLII by Hodder & Stoughton Ltd

Designed and Produced for Brockhampton Press by
Open Door Limited
Rutland, UK

Illustrator: F. Stocks May
Colour separation: GA Graphics Stamford

Title: BLACKBERRY FARM, Emily the Goat
ISBN:1-84186-011-5

EMILY
THE GOAT

Jane Pilgrim

Illustrated by F. Stocks May

BROCKHAMPTON PRESS

Emily was a very nice goat. She had a light-brown shaggy coat, two little horns and a neat little beard. She was born at Blackberry Farm in a bad snowstorm. Mr and Mrs Smiles and their children, Joy and Bob, were very excited.

But Emily's mother could not
feed her, so Mrs Smiles gave her a
bottle. Soon Joy learnt to feed her
too. And sometimes Bob fed her.

EMILY THE GOAT

When Emily was two years old
she had a baby of her own, a little
Billy-goat, which Joy and Bob
loved. But there was not enough
food at Blackberry Farm for two
goats, so Billy went to live with
some friends down the road.

Emily was a very good goat, and she gave Mrs Smiles as much milk as she could. Two jugfuls in the morning, and two jugfuls at night.

Sometimes Naughty George, the Blackberry Farm kitten, would be there at milking-time – hoping for a little extra milk, and Emily would give him a drop. And when Mrs Nibble's baby bunnies were all in bed with measles, Emily would find a little extra for her too.

So everyone at Blackberry Farm
was very fond of Emily, because
she was such a kind, helpful goat.

Then one day Mr Smiles was very worried, and scratched his head and racked his brains and wondered what to do. He told his trouble to Mrs Smiles as she was milking Emily. "There is a little lamb in the field, and her mother has no milk for her. I am afraid she will die."

"We must feed her with a bottle," Mrs Smiles said. "Bring her up to me." So Mr Smiles went down to the field. Little Martha, the lamb, was crying sadly because she was so hungry, and Mr Smiles picked her up and brought her straight to Mrs Smiles.

"I don't know where we are going to get any more milk," Mrs Smiles said: "unless Emily can help us." Emily looked at Little Martha in Mrs Smiles's arms, and she thought hard. Then she turned to Mrs Smiles and said: "I'll try very hard, Mrs Smiles – but I must have more to eat." So, everyone at Blackberry Farm went looking for more food for Emily.

Mrs Nibble and Walter Duck

brought some fresh green leaves.

Mother Hen and Lucy Mouse
found her some extra corn
and maize.

And Mrs Squirrel gave her

some nuts.

Then in the evening, after Mrs
Smiles had milked Emily, there
were THREE jugfuls of milk. Mrs
Smiles was very pleased with
Emily. "You are a dear, good goat,"
she said. "Now we are able to give
Little Martha her bottle."

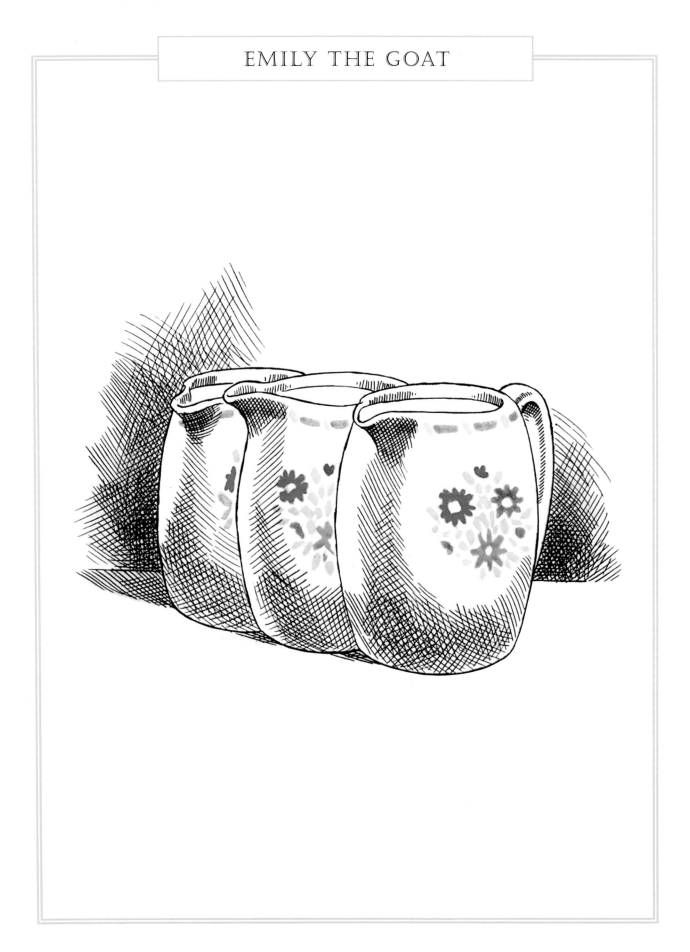

So every day Mrs Nibble and
Mother Hen and Walter Duck and
Lucy Mouse and Mrs Squirrel all
brought a little something for
Emily. And every day Emily gave
Mrs Smiles a little extra milk. And
Mr and Mrs Smiles, and Joy and
Bob, all told her what a dear, good
goat she was. And Emily was very
happy at Blackberry Farm.